JOSEPH HAYDN

SYMPHONY NO. 88

G major / G-Dur / Sol majeur
Hob. I:88

Edited by / Herausgegeben von
Ernst Praetorius

Ernst Eulenburg Ltd

London · Mainz · Madrid · New York · Paris · Tokyo · Toronto · Zürich

JOSEPH HAYDN
Symphony No. 88 in G major

Symphony No. 88 was probably composed in 1787, and it is much the most popular of the five written between the 'Paris' set and the 'London' symphonies. Haydn sent it (together with No. 89) to Johann Tost, a violinist living in Paris; at one time he had been a member of Haydn's orchestra at Esterházy. Tost sold the two symphonies to the Paris publisher Sieber, together with the Op. 54 and Op. 55 string quartets, and Sieber published all these works in parts in or about 1788. In July of the following year the symphonies were also published in Vienna by Artaria, and in 1790 by Longman and Broderip in London, André in Offenbach/Main, and by Hummel in Berlin and Amsterdam. Some of these editions lack trumpet and drum parts, but they appear in the autograph (now in the Esterházy Archives at Budapest).

The present score was edited in 1936 by Dr. Ernst Praetorius from two scores that had belonged to the publisher André, and from which, presumably, André produced his set of parts in 1790.

Wahrscheinlich wurde die Sinfonie Nr. 88 im Jahre 1787 komponiert. Unter den fünf zwischen den 'Pariser' und 'Londoner' geschriebenen Sinfonien ist sie bei weitem die bekannteste. Haydn sandte diese Sinfonie (sowie Nr. 89) an einen Geiger namens Johann Tost in Paris, der früher ein Mitglied von Haydns Orchester in Esterházy gewesen war. Tost verkaufte beide Sinfonien, sowie die Streichquartette Op. 54 und 55, an den Pariser Verleger Sieber, der alle diese Werke in Stimmen in oder um Jahre 1788 veröffentlichte. Im Juli des folgenden Jahres wurden die Sinfonien ebenfalls bei Artaria in Wien verlegt, und 1790 erschienen sie dann bei Longman and Broderip in London, André in Offenbach am Main und Hummel in Berlin und Amsterdam. In einigen dieser Ausgaben fehlen Trompeten- und Paukenstimmen, die aber im Originalmanuskript enthalten sind, das sich jetzt im Esterházy Archiv in Budapest befindet.

Die vorliegende Partitur wurde im Jahre 1936 von Dr. Ernst Praetorius herausgegeben. Er berief sich dabei auf zwei Partituren, die dem Verleger André gehört hatten, und die André vermutlich als Vorlage für die im Jahre 1790 erschienenen Stimmen gedient hatten.

Roger Fiske

Symphony, No. 88

I

Joseph Haydn
1732-1809

4

6

E.E.3659

E.E.3659

14

20

E.E.3659

II

22

E. E. 8659

E. E. 3659

26

E.E. 3659

E.E.3659

Menuetto
Allegretto

Trio

IV

Finale
Allegro con spirito

E.E.3659

42

E. E. 3659

E. E. 3659